GIFTS from the GROVE

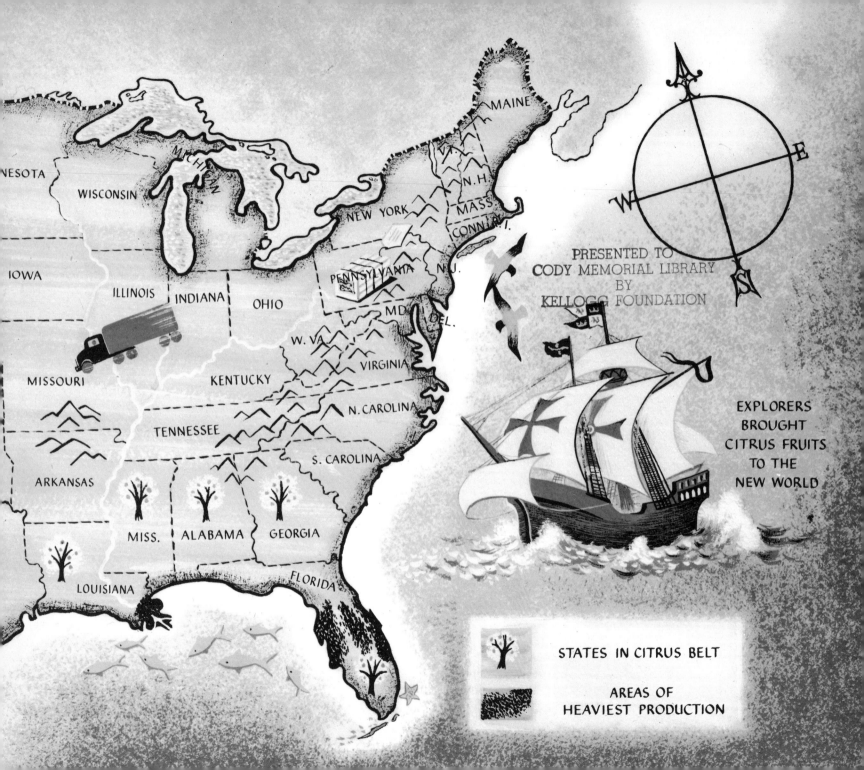

GIFTS from the GROVE

by GERTRUDE WALLACE WALL

PHOTOGRAPHY BY
JOHN CALVIN TOWSLEY
AND OTHERS

CHARLES SCRIBNER'S SONS
NEW YORK

ACKNOWLEDGMENTS

In the collection and preparation of the material for this book, the author has had the fullest cooperation of men in the citrus industry in Florida, Texas, Arizona, and California. To list all of those individuals who have assisted her in this research would require several pages, but to all of them she wishes to express her deepest appreciation.

For the information on the industry in Florida, she is especially indebted to Dr. A. F. Camp, of the Citrus Experiment Station of the University of Florida. His booklet, "Citrus Industry in Florida," was her source of factual material for that area. Dr. Camp's invaluable assistance is gratefully acknowledged.

W. H. Friend, Associate County Agent for Citrus in the Lower Rio Grande Valley, Texas, and Robert Hilgeman, Associate Horticulturist of the University of Arizona Citrus Experiment Farm, supplied authentic source material from their areas.

To D. M. Anderson, Secretary of the Sunkist Growers in California and Arizona, the author is greatly indebted. All resources at his command were generously made available to the author, including photographs to supplement those of Mr. Towsley.

J. C. Johnston, Extension Citrus Specialist for the University of California and the United States Department of Agriculture, who has written the foreword, has guided and advised the author in her search for information on the industry in all the citrus growing areas. He has helped with the background material and the over-all picture.

The cooperation of her photographer son-in-law, John C. Towsley, has made this picture-story of citrus possible. His clear-cut, detailed photographs form the framework of the book.

For criticism of the manuscript and verification of the processes and facts presented herein, the author is indebted to Dr. A. F. Camp, D. M. Anderson, and J. C. Johnston, all of whom gave generously of their time to read and check it.

G. W. W.

Grateful acknowledgment is made for permission to use the following:

Photographs on pages 9, 15, 19, 26, 27, 29, 30, 32, 33, 43, 51, 52, 57, 59, 61, 63, 67, 68, 73, 75, 87, 93, and 94 by *John Calvin Towsley*

Photographs on title page, 11 (large picture), 22, 24, 37, 40 (lower picture), 45, 54, 65, 71, 72, 77, 81, 83, 85, 86, 89, and 91 by *Sunkist Photo*

Photographs on pages 21, 35, 39, 40 (upper picture), 49, and 69 from the *University of Florida Citrus Experiment Station* files

Photograph on page 47 from the *University of California Citrus Experimental Station*, Riverside, California

Photograph on page 79 from the *Florida Division, Food Machinery and Chemical Corporation*, Lakeland, Florida

Photographs on pages 11 (small picture) and 23 from *Lower Rio Grande Valley*, Weslaco, Texas

Photograph on page 12 from SHIPS IN DESIGN, by *Doris Rosenthal*, Brown-Robertson, Co., 1938

Photograph on page 13 from the *California Historical Society*

Map by *Jean Martinez*

TO MY HUSBAND
*whose loyal support and advice
have been most helpful*

CONTENTS

FOREWORD

It has been a pleasure to read Mrs. Gertrude Wall's book on the citrus industry of the United States. It gives an accurate and interesting account of our most important fruit industry. Although citrus fruits are produced in very limited areas of our country, they are available to everyone in fresh or processed form, even in the more remote places.

The American people consume more citrus fruit than any other kind of fruit; in fact, 40 per cent of all fruit consumed is citrus. This indicates the great importance of this industry, not only to the grower of citrus fruit but also to the country as a whole. This widespread use has come about as a direct result of the general appreciation of the refreshing flavor and health-giving qualities of these fruits.

I recommend this book to all who would learn about citrus fruits, where they come from, how they are produced, and how they reach our tables and lunch boxes.

J. C. Johnston
Extension Citrus Specialist
UNIVERSITY OF CALIFORNIA AND
UNITED STATES DEPARTMENT OF AGRICULTURE

The Citrus Family

This is the story of the citrus family. Its first home was in Southeastern Asia. Long before Columbus discovered the New World, citrus fruit was known in parts of the Old World. About the same time, too, the people in China were writing books about their country, their customs, and their plants. They made many simple but lovely drawings of some of the things they wrote about. One of the plants they wrote about and made drawings of was the citron.

The citron grew on a beautiful tree with dark green, glossy leaves. The golden fruit was a little larger than a lemon, and it had a thick rind. The oil from the rind was used to make medicines and perfumes. This citron tree was a favorite in the palace gardens of the emperors because it was lovely as well as useful.

The citron was the first fruit of the citrus family that we know anything about. And we still use it. The rind is candied and put in cookies and cakes. Today there are many members in the citrus family. This book is going to tell you about the three most important ones. They are the orange, the lemon, and the grapefruit. You will find out how and where these citrus fruits are grown, how they are handled, and some of the wonderful products made from them. When we say "citrus" in our story, we mean all three of these fruits. They all have much the same history and the same habits of growth. All of them live in warm, sunny climates.

The children in this picture are in a grove of Valencia oranges. There are many different kinds of oranges. This variety is unusual because it bears both blossoms and fruit at the same time, as you can see in the picture. Most trees do not do this.

Citrus Travels

Southeastern Asia, the native home of the citrus family, has a tropical climate. It is very hot, and the rainfall is heavy. Isn't it surprising, then, to see citrus growing today in colder, drier climates?

In its long history many changes have taken place in the citrus family. It has traveled thousands of miles. Men from western Europe began trading with the people of Asia and the Far East. Some went overland, and others sailed in ships. They brought back to Europe many things which they found among the people of Asia. The citron pleased them greatly. It was unlike anything they had ever seen. They carried it back to Europe and planted it along the shores of the Mediterranean Sea.

The climate in the citron's new home was colder than in the tropics. The trees had to be protected from the cold winter weather. People who could afford it built greenhouses for their trees. Only those trees in the warmest places along the seacoast and those in the greenhouses lived. But the citron had moved to Europe to stay.

The lemon, the orange, and the lime were brought into Europe some time later. They probably came from Southeastern Asia too.

From Europe these fruits were carried westward to the New World by the early explorers. It is thought that Columbus brought some of them to the West Indies.

Grapefruit did not follow the same path as its citrus brothers. It came to America much later. It was brought into Florida from the West Indies. It is thought that the grapefruit had its origin there instead of in Europe or Asia.

How Citrus Fruit Came to Florida

Wherever Spanish settlers landed in the New World, they planted citrus seeds. They had found that if they took citrus fruit with them on their long sea voyages, it would keep them from having scurvy. Around their first settlement in the United States, at St. Augustine, Florida, orange trees were growing by 1579. The Indians liked this fruit too. They ate it, and as they traveled through the forests, they dropped some of the seeds. Soon wild orange trees began to appear among the other trees. Later many of these trees were the beginnings of some of the early groves.

These early groves were planted along the seacoasts and rivers to be near transportation by water. The fruit was shipped by boat to New York and other cities on the Atlantic Coast. It was a luxury and a great treat to the people in colder parts of the country.

Citrus was not taken into California until 200 years after it was started in Florida. Then it came from Mexico. The story of citrus in California is part of the story of the early Spanish missions. The padres, or priests, brought it with them when they traveled north from Mexico into California to make their mission settlements. This is a picture of Mission Santa Barbara. Lovely groves cover the rolling hills around this mission today.

The first orange tree in California was planted at the San Diego Mission by the Franciscan padres. The first orange grove of any size in California was planted at the San Gabriel Mission in 1805. In 1841 the first commercial grove was planted near the place where the Los Angeles railroad station now stands.

How Citrus Fruit Came to California

A Traveler from Brazil

Unlike most varieties of oranges, the navel orange was not brought into this country by the Spanish settlers. It came from Bahia, Brazil. It was brought from there to the Department of Agriculture in Washington, D.C., in 1869. The men in the agriculture department were very interested in this orange because it had no seeds.

A lady named Mrs. Eliza Tibbets wished to start citrus trees around her new home in the Riverside colony in California. She sent to Washington for some young navel orange trees. She planted them in 1873. Her trees produced such fine fruit that nurserymen were eager to get cuttings from them to start new trees. Mrs. Tibbets' two trees became the parents of many navel orange groves in California. Today the navel is one of the two most widely grown varieties there. Some navel oranges are grown in Arizona too, and Florida has begun to develop them.

This is a picture of one of the two original trees in Riverside. It still bears fruit. The iron fence is to protect the tree from people who might pick its fruit.

The navel orange looks different from all other varieties because it has a "navel" formation in the end opposite the stem. This navel is really a tiny orange growing in the end of the larger orange.

The map on the next page shows you all the important citrus areas in the United States. It also shows the Citrus Belt—the states in which the fruit can be grown.

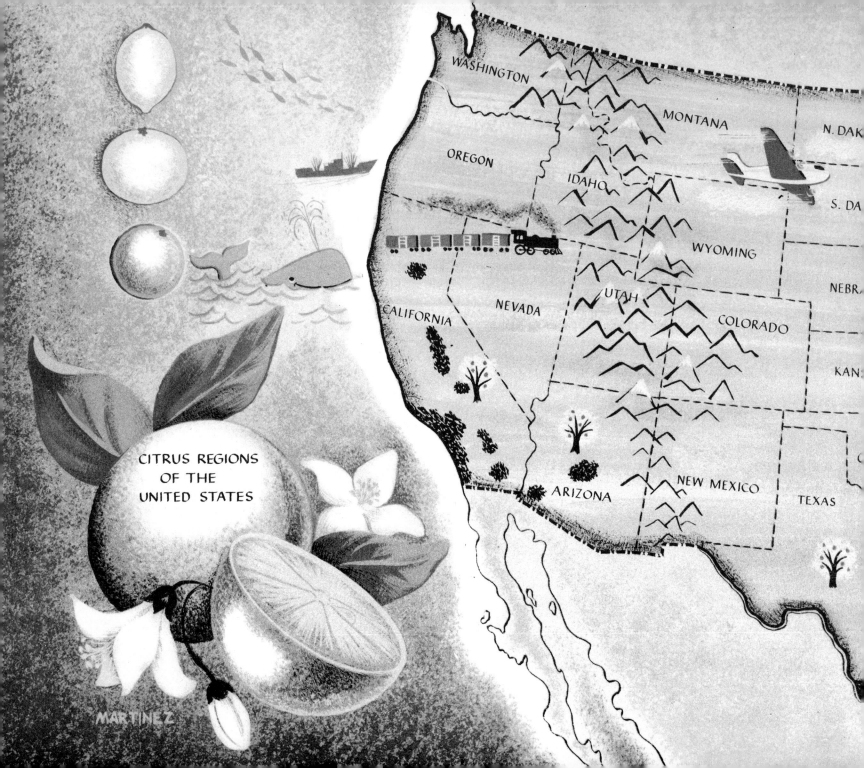

CITRUS REGIONS
OF THE
UNITED STATES

MARTINEZ

WASHINGTON

OREGON

MONTANA

N. DAK

IDAHO

S. DA

CALIFORNIA

NEVADA

WYOMING

UTAH

NEBR

COLORADO

KAN

ARIZONA

NEW MEXICO

TEXAS

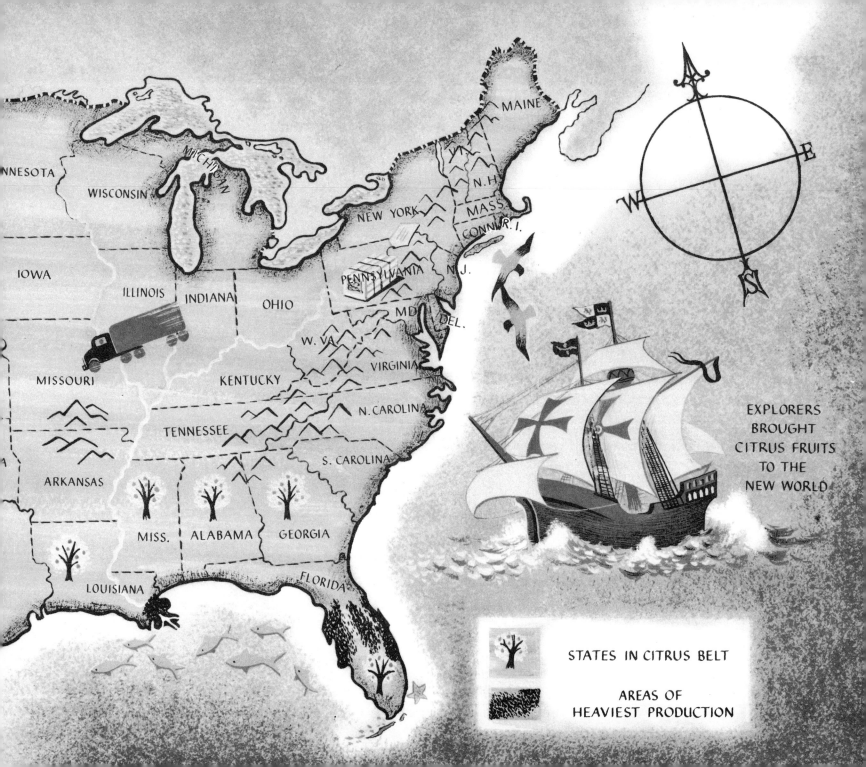

MINNESOTA

WISCONSIN

MICHIGAN

MAINE

VT.

N.H.

NEW YORK

MASS.

CONN. R.I.

IOWA

ILLINOIS

INDIANA

OHIO

PENNSYLVANIA

N.J.

MD.

DEL.

MISSOURI

KENTUCKY

W. VA.

VIRGINIA

N. CAROLINA

TENNESSEE

S. CAROLINA

ARKANSAS

MISS.

ALABAMA

GEORGIA

LOUISIANA

FLORIDA

W

E

S

EXPLORERS
BROUGHT
CITRUS FRUITS
TO THE
NEW WORLD

STATES IN CITRUS BELT

AREAS OF
HEAVIEST PRODUCTION

California—

Land of Citrus Groves, Sunshine, and High Mountains

Along the eastern side of California lie the Sierra Nevada Mountains. Their tallest peaks are snow-capped much of the year. Along the west coast is the Coast Range. These mountains are not so high as the Sierras. Between the two mountain ranges lie hot, fertile valleys. It is in these valleys and along the southern coastal plains that most of California's citrus is grown.

Citrus is also grown in the southern part of California near an inland body of water called the Salton Sea. It is more than 200 feet below sea level. To the north of the Salton Sea is the Coachella Valley. The Imperial Valley is at its southern end. These valleys were desert lands until water was brought from the Colorado River to irrigate the land. Since there is plenty of water in this land now, many citrus groves cover this section.

Florida—

Land of Citrus Groves, Sunshine, and Many Lakes

The first citrus groves in Florida were planted along the seacoast. Now the largest growing area is in the central part of the state. There are many lakes which provide water to make the young trees grow and produce good fruit. The semi-tropical climate makes the citrus feel right at home. If cold air or freezing temperatures do come to Florida, the high, sandy ridges help to keep these enemies from the groves.

Florida citrus growers developed a new orange a little over thirty years ago. It is the Temple orange. This is Florida's best orange for eating because it is easy to peel. The peel has a deep red color, and the orange itself is a deep orange color.

Arizona

In 1707 a few plantings of citrus were made in Arizona, but there were no large groves until 200 years later. Today there are two citrus-growing centers in this state. One of them is around Phoenix. The other is in the very southwestern part of Arizona, near Yuma. Irrigation water from the Gila and Colorado rivers has made it possible to raise citrus here.

Texas

    The Lower Rio Grande Valley, at the very tip end of Texas, is another citrus-growing area in the United States. Although oranges and lemons are grown in Texas, grapefruit grown in this valley are some of the finest in the world. This small part of Texas is the home of the Texas Pink and the Ruby Red grapefruit.

Grapefruit

and

Its

Citrus

Brothers

The name grapefruit probably came from the fact that the fruit often hangs on the trees in bunches like grapes. In this picture the grower is showing such a cluster on his tree. Grapefruit are larger than oranges and are flattened on the end opposite the stem. The skin is yellow, and the flesh is light yellow, pink, or red. The blossoms and leaves are much the same as those of the orange. Another name for grapefruit is "pomelo." It is grown in all the citrus regions you have seen on the map, but it likes the hot desert areas best.

The lemon is yellow and shaped like an egg. The end opposite the stem is quite pointed. Its blossoms look like those of the orange and grapefruit, except that the backs of the white petals have a purple tinge. Its leaves are lighter green than orange and grapefruit leaves. Most of the lemons grown in the United States come from Southern California. Florida is planting more lemon trees each year.

Oranges are grown in all of the citrus regions. However, there are different varieties in the various areas. The navel orange is grown mostly in California and Arizona. The winter orange in the West is the navel. It ripens from November to May. The summer orange, in California, is the Valencia. It ripens from April to November. This orange is also grown in Florida along with a number of other varieties such as the Temple, the Hamlin, the pineapple, the Homosassa, and others. Some Valencia oranges are grown in Texas.

The shipping season in Florida is from October through August. In Arizona it is from November through May. California, with its summer and winter oranges, ships fruit the year round. In Texas the season is from September through February.

Young Trees Are Started

The picture on the opposite page shows a seedbed in a nursery. Now let us see how young citrus trees are started and what happens to them as they grow to produce fruit for us.

Oranges, lemons, and grapefruit are grown and cared for in the same way until the fruit is ready to pick. There are some differences in the picking and in the handling at the packing house. Because oranges are the most widely used, we shall follow their culture throughout our story. As we come to the processes where the three fruits differ, we shall tell you about them.

Young seedlings are started from seed sown thickly in rows in the seedbed. They must be kept well watered and in a warm place. In three or four weeks the tiny plants appear. When they have grown in the seedbed for about a year, they will be transplanted to the nursery row. There they will be set farther apart to give them more room to grow. After a year in the nursery row they will be "budded," as you will see in the next pictures. The plants in the picture on the opposite page are about ready to transplant to the nursery row.

The small picture shows how a young seedling grows. Each seedling has a very long, straight main root. This is called the "tap root." Special care must be taken not to break or bend this root in transplanting.

A good many years ago, growers began to improve on the early seedling varieties brought to this country by the Spaniards. To do this they selected their best varieties and budded them onto the rootstocks of other varieties. A grower in Florida was the first to start this practice. He budded sweet orange trees onto the rootstock of the sour orange trees. The results were so successful that other growers did the same thing. Today all citrus trees are budded, giving us the very best citrus varieties possible.

Budding

Now we shall see how budding is done.

Seeds of strong, vigorous varieties are planted in the nurseries for the seedling rootstock. Usually these varieties do not produce good fruit. Their purpose is to give the trees a strong root system and a good start. When these seedlings are about one and a half to two years old, the tops are budded over to a variety that bears fine fruit. This combination makes a hardy tree that produces a good fruit. Its root is of one variety. Its top is of another variety.

These pictures show the steps in budding.

(1) The worker cuts a bud from a stick of "budwood" taken from a tree that bears fine fruit. This is a shield-shaped piece of bark and wood about an inch long. It has a smooth, flat underside. Notice that a bud has already been removed from this stick of budwood near the end. There may be several buds on one stick.

(2) Then a T-shaped cut is made in the bark of the young seedling about four to six inches above the ground.

(3) The bud is now put into the T-shaped slit and pushed in place underneath the bark of the seedling rootstock.

(4) It must then be held tightly against the "sapwood" of the rootstock so that the sap will flow into it and start its growth. The sapwood is that layer of wood just underneath the bark of a tree. The sap flows through this layer and carries food from the roots to the rest of the tree. The young tree is then firmly wrapped with tape both above and below the bud. The slit must be completely covered.

The bud and its growth are called the "scion."

Growing

and

Shipping

Young Trees

When the bud starts to grow, the seedling top is cut off just above the bud. This sends all the plant food into the bud and forces it to make a new top for the tree. The new shoot is then tied to a stake to keep it growing straight.

After budding, the trees are left in the nursery row for a year. Then they are dug and "balled," ready to set out in a young grove. "Balled" means that the ball of earth around the roots is wrapped in burlap and securely tied for shipping.

This picture shows trees that have been budded in the nursery row and one tree that is balled and ready to be sold. In his left hand the nurseryman holds a budded tree just above the bud. In his right hand he holds a balled tree. In front of the balled tree is a seedling that has just been topped above the bud shoot. At the left in the picture is the budded tree tied to its stake.

A young citrus grove should bear fruit when the trees are four or five years old. As the trees become larger and older, they will bear more. At ten years of age the grove is producing its full amount of fruit.

Irrigation in the Southwest

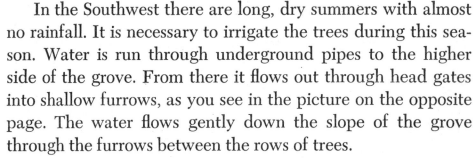

In the Southwest there are long, dry summers with almost no rainfall. It is necessary to irrigate the trees during this season. Water is run through underground pipes to the higher side of the grove. From there it flows out through head gates into shallow furrows, as you see in the picture on the opposite page. The water flows gently down the slope of the grove through the furrows between the rows of trees.

There are little metal gates on the sides of the head gate. These slide up or down to control the amount of water flowing out of each opening. They are called "diamond gates," probably because of the shape of their openings. Other types of head gates are used, but this type is the least wasteful of water. That is important in this dry land.

Another type of irrigation in this area is a sprinkling system. Tall, overhead sprinklers throw water out over the tops of the trees in much the same way that a lawn is sprinkled.

Irrigation in Florida

Florida has more rain than the Southwest, therefore less irrigation is needed. Some groves need no irrigation at all. There are many lakes and, in some places, artesian (flowing) wells to provide the water. Because their water supply is so close at hand, growers in Florida do not have to lay miles of concrete pipe underground to carry water to their groves. They use a pump mounted on a truck so that it can be moved about to nearby lakes or wells. Sections of metal pipe that fit together are laid on top of the ground to make a sprinkling system. Water is then pumped from the nearest lake or well onto the grove through this pipe line.

Our picture shows you just such an irrigation system at work in Florida.

Cultivation — a Disk Cultivator at Work in the West

The disk cultivator shown in this picture gets its name from the revolving disks that cut and turn the soil. It is also used to work weeds and "cover crops" into the ground. Some growers plant crops between their trees just so they can cut and work them back into the soil. As they decay, they keep the soil in good condition. They are really a "green fertilizer."

A shield covers one side of the cultivator. There is also a shield over the tractor treads. These protect the low, overhanging branches from injury when the cultivator is working close to the trees.

In addition to the green fertilizer, the grower must add a manufactured fertilizer to his soil. Citrus trees need many food elements, just as you need many vitamins. The grower must find out what elements his soil needs. Then he adds them in the form of dry or liquid fertilizers. Both the green and the manufac-

tured fertilizers are worked into the soil. Liquid fertilizers are added to the water that is used to irrigate the groves.

In groves where the soil is heavy, cultivating machinery sometimes packs the ground. The packing forms a hard layer of earth underneath the cultivated ground. This is called a "plow sole." Water soaks through the cultivated ground and down to that hard layer of ground. But it runs off before it gets to the tree roots, and the trees are left thirsty.

To keep this from happening, many growers now use a method of "non-cultivation." They spray the ground between the trees with a chemical weed killer. This kills all the weeds, so no cover crops are planted. These growers do not need to use a cultivator. They use a liquid fertilizer instead. The ground looks bare, just like that in the irrigation picture on page 33.

Cultivation — a "Cover Crop Chopper" at Work in Florida

A cultivator like this is used in Florida. It gets its name from the long, knife-like cutting blades which run lengthwise on the revolving drum. These blades chop the cover crops. Can you see how the weight of the heavy roller pushes the chopped material into the soil?

In the West cover crops are planted in the fall so that they will grow during the winter rainy season. They are disked under in the spring. Then they do not take the much-needed moisture in the soil away from the trees during the dry summer season. Instead, the broken-up plant material helps to hold the moisture in the soil.

In Florida the wet and dry seasons are the opposite of those in California and Arizona. Florida summers are wet, and their winters are dry. Therefore their cover crops are planted in the spring and grown during the wet summer season. In the fall they are disked under. Often just the natural weeds and grasses are allowed to grow as a cover crop. Then it is not necessary for the growers to make a special planting.

To add an extra amount of green fertilizer to their soil, Florida growers usually mow or chop their cover crops once during the summer as well as in the fall. Another value of the cover crop in Florida is that it protects the ground in the groves from the heat of the summer sun.

In Texas the growers allow weeds and grass to grow in the citrus groves. These add food elements to the soil. When they are left on top of the ground, these cover crops keep the soil from getting too hot in the summer. Growers mow or drag down these weeds and grasses several times each year so that as much moisture as possible can reach the roots of the trees.

Fighting

Insect

Pests

and

Diseases

How would you like to ride between the rows of orange trees on one of these big machines? Both of them are used to spray the trees to get rid of insects which eat the fruit and the leaves. The spray looks like water. It is water, but it has oil and chemicals in it too.

Our valuable citrus family has many insect enemies. Some of them like the bark and the blossoms better than the fruit and the leaves. There are other insects that are so small that you would have to have a microscope to see them. They bore into the roots of the trees. The growers know these insects are there because they can see knotty swellings on the roots. The tiny insects live in the swellings, and they steal the food that the trees eat.

The spraying machines in these pictures are modern. Growers used to spray their trees with a hose like the one we use to water grass and flowers. Other growers covered each tree with a big tent. Then they pumped fumigating gas inside the tent. Using these big, new machines is much easier and much quicker.

It is important to cover the whole tree with the spray. It must reach the upper and under sides of the leaves, the fruit, the branches, the trunk, and even the ground under the trees. You can see in the pictures that the spray is very strong, so it will get to all of these parts of the tree.

Insects are not the only enemies that worry the growers who raise citrus fruits. There are many kinds of diseases which are even more dangerous than the insect pests. One kind of disease makes the bark break and curl. Another kind causes the whole top of the tree to die. A fungus growth makes the fruit fall and then rot.

There are animals, too, that harm the trees. They burrow underground and damage the roots. The gopher does this in the West, and the salamander is the pest in Florida.

There are men in the different agricultural colleges in our country who spend their time making tests for new kinds of sprays. They want to help the growers in their fight against these enemies of citrus fruits. They test and develop new sprays all the time, and they try to find new and better ones that will destroy these enemies.

41

The Weather Bureau Helps

Have you ever thought how many people help grow citrus? The nurseryman starts the trees. Then the grower buys them and sets them out in his grove. He needs many helpers to irrigate, cultivate, and spray his trees. When the fruit is ripe, he will need more help to pick it. But not all of the nurseryman's helpers work in the grove.

You have just read how men in the agricultural colleges work for the citrus growers. People in other places work for them too. Some of these people travel around and visit the different groves. They have studied citrus culture and are able to help the grower with his problems. They are called farm advisers.

There is one important helper to whom the citrus grower listens but doesn't see. Can you guess who he is? He is the weatherman. He is called a meteorologist. In this picture you see him with his weather maps and instruments. Each day he makes a new map. He receives weather reports hourly from other weather stations around him and from ships at sea. From this information he makes his map, and forecasts the weather in his district for the next twenty-four hours.

Each evening during the winter season he forecasts over the radio. He gives the temperature for the night and early morning hours. He gives the "dew point." That is the temperature at which the moisture condenses out of the air and forms drops of water on the cold surfaces of plants and other objects. He gives the high and low temperatures to be expected in each citrus district, and the hour when there will be the greatest drop. If the breeze goes down suddenly, the temperature may fall as much as 8° in fifteen minutes.

Snow on the Mountains

Imagine a day in California when snow has fallen on the nearby mountains. The grower looks at the beautiful scene, but he is worried. Cold nights are sure to follow in the valleys. The citrus crop may be destroyed. He and his helpers now have a day of hard work ahead of them to get ready for their battle with the cold. They are going to heat the outdoors!

Heating the Outdoors — California

Night comes. The workers in the grove are tired and dirty from their heavy day's work. The heaters which are scattered through the grove have now been filled with oil and are ready to light quickly. There is a double row of heaters along the side toward the mountains. That is the direction from which the cold air will come. Usually there are 45 or 50 heaters to an acre of trees. All day the radio has been tuned to the weather forecast. There will be little sleep for the grower or his workers.

At 8 o'clock the fruit frost warning is tuned in. A steady drop in temperature is expected. Citrus fruits freeze at 27°–30° F., depending upon the kind of citrus and the ripeness of the fruit. Ripe lemons freeze at about 2° higher temperature than ripe oranges or grapefruit. Now that the grower has had the forecast for his district, he must depend upon his thermometers to check the temperature in his own grove during the night.

Thermometers are scattered through the grove. They are attached to wooden shelters on tall posts. The open side of the shelter always faces north so that the sun can never strike it. If the grove is large, the grower has at least one of these thermometers for each five acres of trees. Cold air, like water, flows into low places. The thermometers in these places must be carefully watched.

Sometimes the thermometer in the coldest place is connected with an alarm bell which rings in the grower's house. It is set to go off a few degrees above the danger point. When it rings, the grower knows that there is danger in his grove. He then checks the other thermometers in the grove. If he finds that temperatures in other parts of the grove are dangerously low also, he calls his workers by telephone. They rush to his aid, ready to light the heaters.

Sometimes wind machines are used too, and then the number of heaters can be cut to about fifteen or twenty to an acre. On frosty nights the air close to the ground is colder than the air above the trees. Wind machines mix the warm air with the cold air and keep it moving. In this way the temperature of the air is raised above the danger point. In the picture you can see the heaters and the wind machine.

Heating the Outdoors —

Florida

If you were visiting a citrus fruit grove in Florida, and the weather bureau forecast freezing temperatures, you would see something entirely different. You might think that the growers were going to have a wiener roast. They burn logs to heat the air because wood is cheaper and easier to get than oil. The workers build about 70 fires to an acre. A double row of fires is placed along the north and west sides since those are the directions from which the cold air comes.

Each worker carries a lighter which looks like a big oil can. It holds a gallon of gasoline and oil mixed together. A wick in the end of the spout is kept lighted. When the can is tipped, a few drops of this mixture run down the spout onto the wood, and the wick lights it. A screen in the spout keeps the fire from flashing back into the can. The workers use a lighter much like the one that the California growers use to light their heaters.

Picking the Fruit

The days go by, and the fruit grows and ripens. Oranges and grapefruit are tree-ripened. They do not continue to ripen after they are picked as some other kinds of fruit do. The individual states and the Department of Agriculture set up standards for such things as sugar content and juice content. These standards must be met before picking begins.

When the fruit is ready to harvest, a picking crew moves in.

Emptying the Picking Sack

Here you see a picker emptying his sack. The bottom of a picking sack is open so that the fruit can roll smoothly out of that end when it is emptied. To hold it shut while it is being filled, the bottom end is folded up and fastened to hooks on the sides of the bag. At the bottom corners of the bag you will see the rings which fasten into the hooks on its sides. To empty the bag, this folded flap is unhooked and set down in the field box. Then it is gently pulled away from the fruit. This prevents dropping and bruising. Citrus fruit is handled as carefully as eggs. Millions of dollars worth of fruit each year is thus saved from injury which would cause decay.

The picker wears cotton gloves so that his fingernails will not cut the skin of the fruit. Decay soon starts in places where the skin is broken. Clippers are used to cut off the stem. It is cut as close to the fruit as possible without cutting the skin or the "button" on the stem and end next to the fruit. When fruit is pulled from the tree, the stem often pulls off a piece of the skin along with it. In California all citrus fruit is clipped. However, in Florida a method of twisting and pulling the fruit is used quite successfully. It is faster and cheaper, but fruit loss may be greater.

Inspecting the Lemon Pickers' Work

The man in this picture is an inspector. He is inspecting the work of pickers by "sizing" samples of fruit in the boxes. He uses a ring to size the fruit to make sure it is not being picked too small.

Lemons are picked by size rather than color. The picker carries a ring, like the one in the picture, in his left hand. Another small ring attached to the sizing ring slips over his middle finger. This holds the sizing ring in place in his hand. He sizes the fruit before picking it. He picks the green fruit which is too large to go through the ring. That will ripen later in the packing house. He picks all of the yellow fruit.

Unlike oranges and grapefruit, some of the best grades of lemons are picked green. They will keep and ship better than the yellow fruit.

The lemon tree never takes a vacation. It blossoms, grows, and ripens fruit the year round. Therefore we find buds, blossoms, green fruit, and ripe fruit all on the tree at the same time. Picking crews go over the trees every six weeks. This, together with the fact that the fruit must be sized as it is picked, makes lemon picking a slow and expensive business. Picking and packing costs almost twice as much for lemons as for oranges or grapefruit which are not usually sized in the field.

After the fruit is picked, it is taken to the packing house by truck.

This truck has just come from the grove to the packing house with its load of freshly-picked fruit. The driver unloads it onto a moving belt, or conveyor, which carries it into the building.

Every orange you see in a grocery store has a nice, bright orange color. But all oranges don't come off the trees that way. If there hasn't been enough cold weather, the orange color will fail to develop. In the tropics, oranges never become a bright orange because there is no cold weather.

If oranges show a green coloring, they will be stacked in the degreening, or "coloring," rooms for twenty-four to seventy-two hours. There the temperature is kept at 85° F. A small amount of ethylene gas is added to the air in the room to bleach the green. This does not affect the flavor or the quality of the fruit. Oranges which do not need degreening go directly to the washers and start their journey through the packing house.

When grapefruit are unloaded at the packing house, they need no special treatment. They can go at once to the washers. Lemons, though, must be stored three or four days to permit moisture to evaporate out of the skin before they are sent to the washers. Their skins then become firmer and are not so easily injured.

Unloading
Fruit
at the
Packing
House

Where the Fruit Is Processed

This picture gives a general view of these processes.

(1) Rollers over which fruit passes first. Leaves and trash from the grove drop through these rollers. Fruit then moves along on canvas belts.

(2) Dark room. This has a "black" light to show up rot. A worker sits in here and removes from the belt fruit in which spots of decay are shown by this light. (This is not necessary in Florida because their fruit does not have brown rot.)

(3) The pony sizer. At the far end of this row the fruit makes a turn. It rolls over a revolving drum with openings which allow the very small fruit (the "ponies") to drop through. They drop onto another belt which carries them off to a part of the plant where they are weighed. Trucks then take them to the processing plant. The larger fruit moves on its way to the washers.

(4) Soap tank. In this tank soap suds and sometimes a disinfectant are added to remove spray solution and dirt from the field. Rotating wooden paddle rollers, called submergers, push the fruit beneath the water and move it along.

(5) The washer. Rotating brush rollers scrub and clean the fruit.

(6) Rinse tank. Overhead pipes spray the fruit to wash off soapy water and rinse it clean.

(7) Heating tank. Water in this tank is heated to 115°–120° F. to control brown rot. (This process is not necessary in Florida.)

(8) Rinse tank. The fruit is given a final rinse. Lemons then go to storage rooms while they are still wet. Oranges and grapefruit go to the driers.

(9) Brass rollers are used for the first drying.

(10) Hairbrushes and fans for final drying, waxing, and polishing.

The Drying Process

After their thorough washing and rinsing, oranges and grapefruit must be dried. The first step in this process is running the fruit over brass rollers. Rubber wipers on the under side of the rollers remove moisture from them as they revolve.

Pieces of rubber tubing fastened to turning metal bars above the fruit push it gently along. They look like so many fingers at work.

Lemons are not put through the drying process but are taken to air-conditioned storage rooms while still wet. Sometimes they are given a coating of wax emulsion to keep them from shrinking. Then they are sent to the color sorting room. Here they are sorted as to green, light green, silver, and yellow color for storage purposes. The green lemons will keep the longest and the yellow, the shortest length of time. They are usually stored in the packing house for a while to allow coloring and curing.

In Florida, oranges may be passed through a "color added" dye solution before going through the driers. This does not affect the inside of the fruit but adds an orange-red dye to the surface of the peel to make it more attractive. Then it must be stamped "color added." In California and Arizona the degreening room is the approved method of bringing out the coloring.

Grading

Once more our fruit takes up its travel on canvas belts after its water journey. First it goes to the graders. Here it is graded as to appearance. Defects, color, shape, and smoothness of skin are some of the qualities by which it is graded. Each grade goes down a separate chute onto a belt leading to bins of the various grades. Decayed or injured fruit goes into the "cull" chute to be discarded.

Notice that all workers who handle the fruit wear cotton gloves. Fingernail cuts cause heavy fruit loss from decay.

Oranges and grapefruit have moved steadily through the cleaning, drying, and waxing process without a stop. Waxing prevents the skin from drying and shrinking. It makes the fruit keep better. It also makes it shiny and lovely to look at.

After the fruit leaves the grader, it is checked by a fruit inspector. He takes samples off the conveyor as they come along. He cuts them open to see if they are graded properly. Those oranges which are in the top grades will have top brand names. They are very carefully selected for size, appearance, and quality.

Stamping

After leaving the grader, the better grades of oranges are stamped with a brand name. Each orange runs into a slot which carries it under a wheel with a ridged rubber tire. The wheel presses the fruit down on a heated steel stamp bearing the brand name. Beneath the stamp is a little ink pad which re-inks the stamp whenever it is pressed down. This ink will not wash off.

When fruit is stamped, it tells the buyer he has fruit of a good quality. That means it has been carefully graded and sized.

Grapefruit are sometimes stamped. Lemons are not stamped.

After being stamped, oranges and grapefruit are at last ready to be packed.

The Sizer

As oranges and grapefruit move on to the packers, they are sized by means of rollers which gradually spread farther apart. The fruit in this picture is just starting to roll down the line. The small fruit will drop through the sizer first, then the larger and still larger sizes will drop through as the fruit rolls along.

Each size of fruit, as it drops through the sizer, rolls down a chute into a separate canvas bin. In California the fruit is counted by machine. As each fruit leaves the end of the chute, it rolls over an electric counter. This records the number on a machine located near the shipping department. That gives an exact account of the fruit packed for each grower. In Florida the fruit is weighed in when it is brought to the packing house.

Machines are also used for sizing lemons. However, lemons are more irregular in size and shape than oranges and grape-fruit. This makes sizing by machine difficult and some further sizing by the workers is necessary. In some places packers select by sight lemons of about the same size from the conveyor belt as they pack.

Citrus fruits are packed and sold by size. California, Texas, and Arizona use a standard shipping box which has a middle partition to give added strength. In Florida most of the fruit is packed in wirebound crates.

Packing — in the West, the Standard Shipping Box

Packers are paid by the box. The price paid for packing a box varies with the size of fruit packed. Each packer has her own number on her tray, her own bench, and a rubber stamp with her number on it. When she finishes packing a box, she stamps her number on the end of it. Her pay at the end of the day is figured on the number of boxes she has packed, so packers work very fast.

In California and Arizona much fruit is wrapped in tissue paper. Sometimes a box is "face wrapped." That means that only the fruit on the top layer and that facing the cracks is wrapped. Fruit in the center is left unwrapped.

The packer fills her box two or three inches above the top. She then folds pieces of cardboard and places them over the center partition and along the top edges of the box. These cardboards prevent injury to the fruit on the sharp wooden edges. Now she stamps the pack number, as well as her own number, on the end of the box. Then she places it on a roller conveyor and moves to the next bin. This bin contains fruit of a different size. In moving from bin to bin each packer gets her turn at the various sizes of fruit.

At one time Florida packers used the same standard shipping boxes as the ones in use in the West. In the last few years they have largely changed over to the wirebound crate which you see here. It is simpler and cheaper to make. It has no center partition. In it the fruit is packed in layers instead of in a standard pattern. Most of the fruit is not wrapped. The lids are fastened on by means of three wires around the box. One wire is around the middle where the center partition would be in the standard box. The other two wires are placed halfway between this center wire and each end of the box. No expensive box making machines or lidding machines are needed.

Other types of containers are the mesh bag and the cardboard box. The mesh bags are used for small amounts of fruit in retail stores. The cardboard boxes are half the size of the standard shipping box. Their use is increasing because they are cheaper to use and lighter to handle. In them the fruit is not wrapped.

Packing — the Wirebound Crate and Other Containers

Lidding

This picture shows the packed standard box as it moves on the roller conveyor from the packer to the lidding machine. The girl at the left is keeping a record of the packer's number and the pack number stamped on each box as it comes from the packer.

As the box of fruit rolls into place on the machine, the worker takes a lid from the stack at his left. He slides it under the curved plate above the center of the box. He then steps on a foot lever which lowers the nailing machine. It presses the ends of the lid down to meet the ends of the box, and nails the lid in place. Nails slide down the tubes from above. Notice four tubes going to each end of the box. A small machine at the right then fastens a narrow metal strip across the lid just above the center partition. The fruit bulges at the top of the box because it was packed two or three inches above the top. This bulge holds the pack tight.

Now it is ready to be stacked for shipment. Each grade is stacked in a separate pile.

In California the packing house works on only one grower's fruit at a time. In this way they keep an accurate count of the number of boxes of each grade and size for each grower. When the fruit is sold, he is paid for that number.

In Florida the fruit is weighed in when it is brought to the packing house. There it is mixed with the fruit from other groves. Each grower is paid for the tonnage weighed in.

Hand Trucking ,and Shipping

As the packed boxes are removed from the conveyor, they are placed in stacks of four each. Hand truckers pick up these stacks with clamp trucks and move them into refrigerator cars or trucks. Fruit which is to be shipped later will be sent to a cooler in another part of the building. There it is kept at a temperature of 40°–50° F. to prevent spoilage.

The picture shows how the standard boxes are stacked for shipment in a refrigerator car. They are placed on end, and the bulge in the top of each box serves as a cushion to keep the pack tight. Seven boxes are placed in a row across the end of the car. Each row is stacked two boxes high. There are thirty-three rows in a car. That makes 462 boxes in a car.

Wirebound boxes are stacked on their sides. The stacks are usually five boxes high. There are about 440 boxes to the car. This number varies depending upon the size of the car.

Cardboard boxes are "chimney stacked." That means they are laid on top of each other in the same way that bricks are laid in a chimney. The spaces for mortar between the bricks are left as air spaces between the boxes. Citrus fruit must not be shut up airtight. The cardboard boxes have holes in them for the air to circulate.

The small picture shows a large refrigerator truck being loaded. Like the railroads, they may take fruit to any place in the United States or Canada, or to the harbor for shipment to distant lands.

To Market We Go

At last our fruit has found its way to the neighborhood market where you and I may buy it. Citrus fruits are sold by the pound in this market. In many places they are sold by the dozen.

The fruit has been shipped here from the packing houses and citrus "Exchanges." These are the marketing organizations which handle the growers' fruit. Our markets buy through them, and they pay the grower for his fruit.

Tempting looking vegetables and fruit fill the markets today. The oranges make a bright splash of color among the greens, reds, and browns of the other produce. The yellow of the lemons and grapefruit add their bit to the color display too. Citrus fruits are no longer a luxury as they were many years ago. Today we can all have the fruit that was once the special property of kings and queens. They are now so low in price that everyone can have them to enjoy.

One of the children in the picture is carrying a mesh bag of citrus fruit. This is one of the newer methods of packing the fruit for shipment.

Other Uses for Citrus Fruits

When you squeeze an orange, what do you do with the rind and the seeds? Do you throw them away and just drink the juice? If you were to visit a factory which makes orange juice, you would be surprised to see that not one part of the orange is wasted. This factory is called a processing plant.

By "processing" we mean everything that is done to the fruit in this kind of plant. First the juice is taken out, or extracted. This is the main product. Then it must be treated so that it will not spoil. After that it is canned.

There are many men who work in the processing plant. They spend their days trying to think of different things they can make from the part of the orange that is usually thrown away. These men have thought of many products to make from this material that used to be wasted. They call these "by-products." A by-product is anything that is made out of the waste material after the main product is made.

The upper part of this picture shows you the many, many by-products of the three citrus fruits. The lower part of the picture shows a display of samples of some of the by-products. Are you surprised that the three citrus fruits have so many uses?

The by-products are a very important part of the citrus fruit industry. And every day more are being discovered. Many of them are in our food, but we never think about it. Some are used in medicines, soaps, perfumes, fly sprays, and other products we have in our homes. Even the big oil, rubber, and steel industries recognize the importance of citrus fruit by-products.

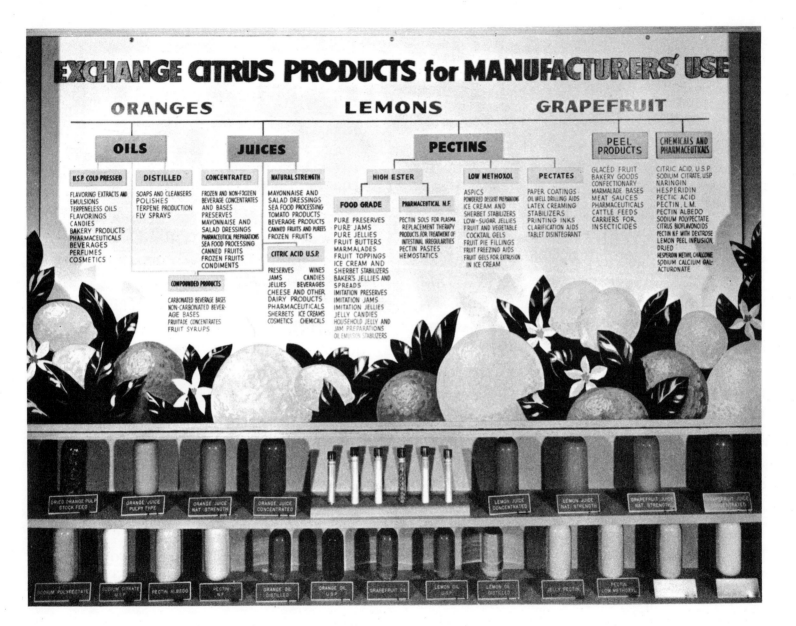

EXCHANGE CITRUS PRODUCTS for MANUFACTURERS' USE

ORANGES   LEMONS   GRAPEFRUIT

OILS

U.S.P. COLD PRESSED

FLAVORING EXTRACTS AND
EMULSIONS
TERPENELESS OILS
FLAVORINGS
CANDIES
BAKERY PRODUCTS
PHARMACEUTICALS
BEVERAGES
PERFUMES
COSMETICS

DISTILLED

SOAPS AND CLEANSERS
POLISHES
TERPENE PRODUCTION
FLY SPRAYS

JUICES

CONCENTRATED

FROZEN AND NON-FROZEN
BEVERAGE CONCENTRATES
AND BASES
PRESERVES
MAYONNAISE AND
SALAD DRESSINGS
PHARMACEUTICAL PREPARATIONS
SEA FOOD PROCESSING
CANNED FRUITS
FROZEN FRUITS
CONDIMENTS

NATURAL STRENGTH

MAYONNAISE AND
SALAD DRESSINGS
SEA FOOD PROCESSING
TOMATO PRODUCTS
BEVERAGE PRODUCTS
CANNED FRUITS AND PUREES
FROZEN FRUITS

COMPOUNDED PRODUCTS

CARBONATED BEVERAGE BASES
NON-CARBONATED BEVER-
AGE BASES
FRUITADE CONCENTRATES
FRUIT SYRUPS

CITRIC ACID U.S.P.

PRESERVES	WINES
JAMS	CANDIES
JELLIES	BEVERAGES

CHEESE AND OTHER
DAIRY PRODUCTS
PHARMACEUTICALS

SHERBETS	ICE CREAMS
COSMETICS	CHEMICALS

PECTINS

HIGH ESTER

FOOD GRADE

PURE PRESERVES
PURE JAMS
PURE JELLIES
FRUIT BUTTERS
MARMALADES
FRUIT TOPPINGS
ICE CREAM AND
SHERBET STABILIZERS
BAKER'S JELLIES AND
SPREADS
IMITATION PRESERVES
IMITATION JAMS
IMITATION JELLIES
JELLY CANDIES
HOUSEHOLD JELLY AND
JAM PREPARATIONS
OIL EMULSION STABILIZERS

PHARMACEUTICAL N.F.

PECTIN SOLS FOR PLASMA
REPLACEMENT THERAPY
PRODUCTS FOR TREATMENT OF
INTESTINAL IRREGULARITIES
PECTIN PASTES
HEMOSTATICS

LOW METHOXOL

ASPICS
POWDERED DESSERT PREPARATION
ICE CREAM AND
SHERBET STABILIZERS
LOW-SUGAR JELLIES
FRUIT AND VEGETABLE
COCKTAIL GELS
FRUIT PIE FILLINGS
FRUIT FREEZING AIDS
FRUIT GELS FOR EXTRUSION
IN ICE CREAM

PECTATES

PAPER COATINGS
OIL WELL DRILLING AIDS
LATEX CREAMING
STABILIZERS
PRINTING INKS
CLARIFICATION AIDS
TABLET DISINTEGRANT

PEEL PRODUCTS

GLACED FRUIT
BAKERY GOODS
CONFECTIONARY
MARMALADE BASES
MEAT SAUCES
PHARMACEUTICALS
CATTLE FEEDS
CARRIERS FOR
INSECTICIDES

CHEMICALS AND PHARMACEUTICALS

CITRIC ACID, U.S.P.
SODIUM CITRATE, USP
NARINGIN
HESPERIDIN
PECTIC ACID
PECTIN, L.M.
PECTIN ALBEDO
SODIUM POLYPECTATE
CITRUS BIOFLAVONOIDS
PECTIN N.F. WITH DEXTROSE
LEMON PEEL INFUSION,
DRIED
HESPERIDIN METHYL CHALCONE
SODIUM CALCIUM GAL-
ACTURONATE

DRIED ORANGE PULP STOCK FEED | ORANGE JUICE PULPY TYPE | ORANGE JUICE NAT. STRENGTH | ORANGE JUICE CONCENTRATED | LEMON JUICE CONCENTRATED | LEMON JUICE NAT. STRENGTH | GRAPEFRUIT JUICE NAT. STRENGTH | CITRUS JUICE CONCENTRATED

SODIUM POLYPECTATE | SODIUM CITRATE U.S.P. | PECTIN ALBEDO | PECTIN N.F. | ORANGE OIL DISTILLED | ORANGE OIL U.S.P. | GRAPEFRUIT OIL | LEMON OIL U.S.P. | LEMON OIL DISTILLED | JELLY PECTIN | PECTIN LOW METHOXYL

The Juice Extractors

Fruit that is to be used for juice need not be handled as carefully as that shipped fresh to markets. It is not put in boxes but is shipped in large quantities in trucks. It comes from both the field and the packing house.

As in the packing house, it goes first to the graders. They take out all split and bruised fruit. This is later added to the "rag" (the inside fruit tissues) and seeds from the juice extractors. The good fruit goes to the washers and sterilizers.

After being thoroughly washed and sterilized, the fruit goes to the juice extractors. Rows and rows of them fill a very large room. In this picture you can see down one row. Notice that you can also see the tops of machines in other rows on each side of this center one.

The platform down tne middle of the picture between the extractors is a walkway for the workmen. It is raised so that they need not walk on the wet, slippery floor. Oranges on the conveyor belts have just come from the washers. Some water drips from them onto the floor.

As the fruit moves along on the conveyor belts, it rolls off into the little slanting ramps at the sides. Each tube of the ramp leads to a single "extractor cup" in the machine. When a fruit drops into this cup, another cup-shaped press closes down on top of it. The sides of the two cups look like many fingers. These mesh together as the fruit is pressed between them to squeeze out the juice. There are many extractor cups in each machine.

When the juice is extracted, it flows off to the vacuum tanks through sealed, stainless steel tubes. The rind, seed, and pulp go to the part of the plant where the by-products are made. We cannot see inside these extractors because they are sealed. This is to keep any dust particles or bacteria from getting into the juice. All the machines and juice containers are lined with stainless steel. Great care is taken to keep the juice free of all kinds of impurities.

New Products

The man in this picture is in a laboratory in the processing plant. He is experimenting with juices. He is trying to find new and better ways of making them. Sometimes he discovers he can make an entirely new product. Such laboratories as this are an important part of a processing plant.

Canned citrus juice of natural, or "single," strength was first put on the market between 1920 and 1930. After it was processed, it did not have quite the same flavor as fresh juice. The chemists thought that this change took place when it was heated for canning. Therefore they worked to improve their product. Finally, in 1945, frozen juice concentrates were developed. These proved to have about the same flavor as fresh juice. The chemists had found a way to take the water out of the juice without heating it. This is done in big vacuum tanks which you will see in a later picture.

Florida growers were the leaders in the juice processing field. They began making frozen juice concentrates in 1945. Most of the Florida fruit is processed. California has large processing plants in the southern part of the state, but most of their fruit is sold fresh.

Fresh orange juice is now being refrigerated and sold to milk companies. There it is bottled and delivered to our doors by the milkman, packed in quart-size containers.

Vacuum Tanks

Have you ever gone camping in the mountains? If you had to boil water to cook your food, you probably found that the food never did get done. Did you wonder why? Water boils at a much lower temperature the higher you go. The water all changes to steam, so the food remains uncooked. The air pressure is much lighter at great heights. At sea level, water boils at 212° F. where the air pressure is fifteen pounds to the square inch of water. If you were to get into a space ship and go up fifty miles, the air pressure would be much, much less. Nothing you would want to cook in your space ship would get done even though the water would boil at 80° F.

To make concentrated fruit juices, this same principle is used. This picture shows a low temperature vacuum tank used in making concentrated juice. It is really several tanks joined together. The juice flows from extractors into these vacuum tanks. The first tank has a temperature of about 75° F., which is room temperature. Then the juice flows from one tank to another. The air pressure in each of these vacuum tanks is less than in the one before. This lack of pressure makes the juice "boil" and lose its moisture at a lower temperature each time it flows into another tank. When it comes out of the last tank, the juice boiled at 50° F.

Chemists found that too much heat destroyed some of the fresh flavor of the orange juice. They used the vacuum tanks and discovered that the juice concentrate got colder instead of hotter. In this way the fresh flavor was kept because it was never "cooked."

The juice is concentrated a little too much so that fresh juice can be added to it. The concentrate flows from the last vacuum tank to a "blender" tank. There the fresh juice is added to make the right "blend," or mix. This gives the concentrate an entirely fresh flavor.

The Filling Machine

From the blender the juice goes to the cooling tanks. There it is cooled down to a thick, freezing slush. Paddles in these tanks keep it moving so that it will not freeze solid. Now it is ready to be put into cans.

Here is a filling machine. Empty cans are moving to it from the left. They are on a conveyor belt. As they travel around the machine, they are filled. Then they move off to the right to the lidding machine. From here they move on into refrigeration where the juice is frozen solid. Then the cans are ready for packing and shipment in refrigerated trucks or railroad cars.

From the time the juice leaves the extractors until it comes out of refrigeration, frozen solid, takes only about a half an hour. Now you can see why it is called "Quick Frozen Concentrate."

Shipping the Juice

Not all the concentrated juices are frozen. Most of the non-frozen juice concentrates and many of the by-products are shipped in barrels. All barrels used for shipping juice are lined with stainless steel.

The men in this picture are loading a freight car. Loading these heavy barrels is done with a "lift truck." The man in the center of the picture, with his back to us, is standing on the platform of the lift truck. He raises or lowers this platform by means of the lever in his right hand. The barrel on the truck platform is being raised into place for stacking. Another barrel is being rolled into place for the truck to pick up next.

The workman in the picture with a pad and a pencil is checking the load and making out the "bill of lading." This will be a list of all the barrels which will be shipped on this freight car.

Using Non-Frozen Juice Concentrates

These boys look happy, don't they? They have just stopped at their neighborhood soda fountain for a big glass of their favorite orange drink. After they finish drinking this, they should be ready for a fast game of baseball.

This picture shows one use of non-frozen juice concentrates. Here the concentrate is used as a base to make an orange-flavored drink. Your mother does much the same thing when she squeezes juice and makes orangeade or lemonade for you at home. She adds water and sugar and maybe some other fruit juice to the orange or lemon juice base. The orange juice at the soda fountain is mixed the same way. No wonder we like it!

Companies that make soft drinks buy concentrates in large quantities. They mix it, bottle it, and sell it to you and me. Probably the barrels you saw in the last picture were going to one of these companies. Just think how many, many bottles of orange or lemon drink one barrel of juice concentrate will make!

The Pectin Sheet

Have you ever watched sheets being ironed on the big roller ironers in a laundry? Perhaps your mother has a roller ironer at home and you have seen that work. This big machine is called a "drum drier." It irons citrus pulp the way the laundry irons sheets. What you see in this picture is a "pectin" sheet. Pectin is the substance that makes jellies and jams "set," or stay firm. Your mother buys it to add to the fruit juice when she makes jelly.

There are many uses for pectin in our food. Bakers use it in pie and cake fillings. Ready-mixed puddings and pie fillings contain pectin. Manufacturers of jellied products use a great deal of it.

Pectin is one of the by-products made from the "rag" (inside tissues) and pulp of citrus fruits after the juice is extracted. Much juice has been evaporated out of the pulp before it gets to this drier. Also, it has been treated with chemicals, bleached, and washed. This is the final drying process. The pulp rolls on a wire mesh screen over this heated, stainless steel drum. The screen holds the pulp in a sheet. Juice squeezed from the pulp is carried away in the covered trough on the floor.

After the pectin is dried, it is put through a grinder. Then it looks like coarse granulated sugar. It is light yellow in color.

In this picture the workman has broken off a handful of the mixture. He will test it in the laboratory. Each batch is tested before it is packaged for shipment. Much of it is shipped in barrels.

Dehydrating Citrus Fruit Pulp

This picture looks like a village street, doesn't it? You might very well call it that, and say that these are machine houses. The machines in the picture are making something new from citrus fruit. They are making a different kind of by-product. It is not for people, but for beef and dairy cattle.

The long round tubes you see are called dehydrators. To "dehydrate" means to dry out. You have probably seen your mother put dried prunes or apricots into a pan of water. Sometimes she lets them soak all night. The next morning, if you look at them, they are fat and soft because they drank a lot of the water they soaked in. Then your mother puts some sugar in this water and cooks the fruit so you can eat it.

These machines do just the opposite thing with the citrus fruit pulp. They take the water out of the pulp to dry it. We say that they dehydrate the pulp. The little brick "house" in front of the drum has a furnace in it. Hot air from the fire in the furnace is blown through the long drum. The citrus pulp inside is tossed and turned about all the time by another drum which turns inside the outer one. This lets the hot air reach every little piece of pulp. As soon as it is completely dry, it comes out at the far end of the drum. Then it is packed into burlap sacks like the one the man is wheeling on the cart in the picture.

All of these burlap sacks full of dehydrated pulp are packed on trucks or in freight cars and shipped to the farmers all over the country. Their beef and dairy cattle will have something new to eat. They will have citrus fruit pulp to make them give even better meat and richer milk and cream.

Cows Like Citrus Too

It's milking time on the dairy farm. The cows have come eagerly into their stanchions. Each cow has her own place. She goes straight into it because she knows a good meal is waiting for her. The farmer is feeding dried citrus pulp to his cattle. He finds that his cows do well on it. And how they like it!

These Boy Scouts like to visit the dairy. They live in the city. To them the dairy is a most interesting place at milking time. As they watch the cows being fed, they learn that no part of the citrus fruit is wasted. Feed for cattle makes use of anything that is left over after food for people is taken out. Chemists at work in their laboratories have done this for the citrus industry. They have developed many new and better products for us all to enjoy.

Citrus Gold

The children in this picture drink a glass of orange juice each morning. Do you suppose they think of the wonderfully exciting story that made it possible for them to have it?

In America we eat more oranges than any other fruit. We use citrus fruits, either fresh or processed, for breakfast, lunch, and dinner. In fact, we use an average of about a pound of oranges per person every week. Fresh citrus fruits, as well as the processed juices, are on the market every month of the year. We need citrus fruits all the year because they supply us with vitamin C and other vitamins and minerals. These help to keep people healthy and strong.

If it had not been for the explorers from the Old World who came to the New World in search of gold, we might never have had citrus fruit. These explorers didn't realize that they left us something even more wonderful than the gold they were looking for on our shores.

INDEX

CITRUS REGIONS
OF THE
UNITED STATES

WASHINGTON
OREGON
MONTANA
N. DAKO
IDAHO
S. DAK
WYOMING
CALIFORNIA
NEVADA
UTAH
COLORADO
NEBRA
KA
ARIZONA
NEW MEXICO

MARTINEZ